KU-630-532

Ladybird books are widely available, but in case of
difficulty may be ordered by post or telephone from:

Ladybird Books – Cash Sales Department
Littlegate Road Paignton Devon TQ3 3BE
Telephone 01803 554761

A catalogue record for this book is available
from the British Library

Published by Ladybird Books Ltd Loughborough Leicestershire UK
LADYBIRD and the device of a Ladybird are trademarks of Ladybird Books Ltd

© The Walt Disney Company MCMXCV
Based on the Pooh stories by A A Milne
(copyright the Pooh Properties Trust)
All rights reserved. No part of this publication may be reproduced,
stored in a retrieval system, or transmitted in any form or by any
means, electronic, mechanical, photocopying, recording or otherwise,
without the prior consent of the copyright owner.

first Disney books

Pooh's
day out

Ladybird

Do *you* like Pooh's umbrella?

umbrella

What is Tigger riding?

bicycle

What colour is Rabbit's ball?

ball

Do *you* have any wellingtons?

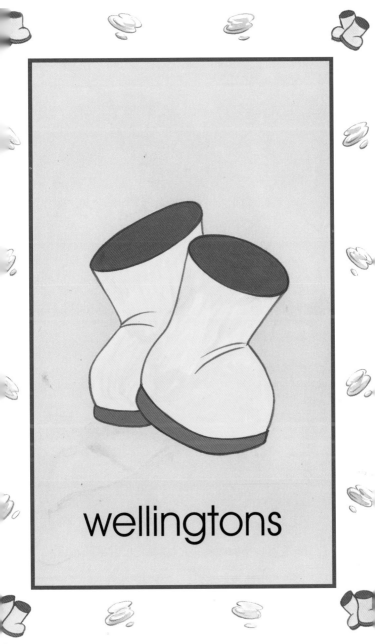

wellingtons

What can *you* see in the sky?

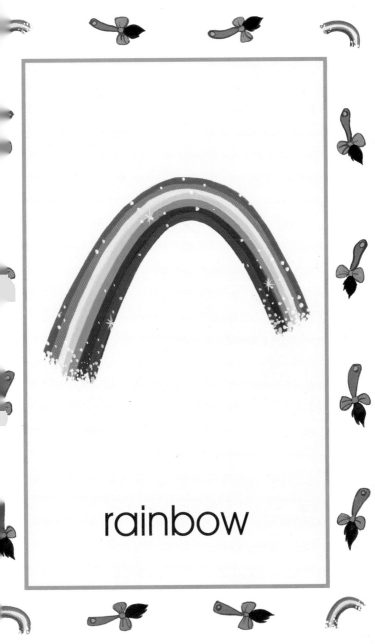

rainbow

What is Pooh holding?

flower

Who is under the tree?

tree

What is Roo playing with?

car

What colour is the sun?

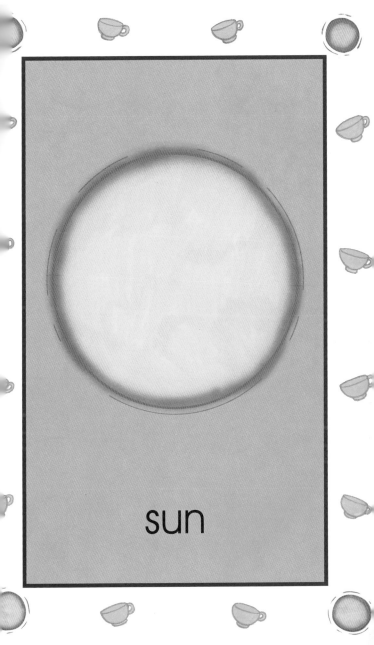

sun

Does Eeyore like the rain?

rain

What is Piglet wearing?

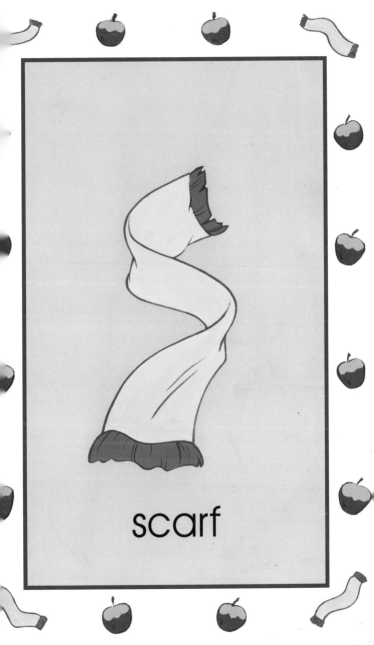

scarf

What is on Pooh's head?

hat